Wishes and Worries

A story to help children understand a parent
who drinks too much alcohol

Produced by the Centre for Addiction and Mental Health (CAMH)

Illustrated by Ben Hodson

camh

Centre for Addiction and Mental Health
Centre de toxicomanie et de santé mentale

A Pan American Health Organization / World Health Organization Collaborating Centre
Affiliated with the University of Toronto

Library and Archives Canada Cataloguing in Publication

Wishes and Worries: a story to help children understand a parent who drinks too much alcohol
produced by Centre for Addiction and Mental Health;
illustrated by Ben Hodson.
(Storybooks for children series; # 2)

Written for children 5-10 years old.
ISBN: 978-0-88868-493-6 (PRINT)
ISBN: 978-0-88868-658-9 (PDF)
ISBN: 978-0-88868-659-6 (HTML)

1. Children of alcoholics–Juvenile fiction.

I. Hodson, Ben
II. Centre for Addiction and Mental Health
III. Series.

PS8600.W58 2005   jC813'.6   C2005-900422-3

Product Code P5599

Printed in Canada

This publication may be available in other formats.
For information about alternate formats or other CAMH publications, or to place an order, please contact Sales and Distribution:

Toll-free: 1 800 661-1111

Toronto: 416 595-6059

E-mail: publications@camh.net

Website: www.camh.net

This book was produced by:

DEVELOPMENT
Susan Rosenstein, CAMH

EDITORIAL
Diana Ballon, CAMH

DESIGN
Anja Kessler, CAMH

PRODUCTION
Christine Harris, CAMH

MARKETING
Rosalicia Rondon, CAMH

2918/03-2009   P5599

ABOUT THIS BOOK

The Centre for Addiction and Mental Health (CAMH) recognizes the need for materials to help children cope with substance use and mental health problems in their families. The Storybooks for Children Series was launched in 2002 with *Can I Catch It Like a Cold? A Story to Help Children Understand a Parent's Depression*. *Wishes and Worries* is the second book in this important series. It is the result of the creative thinking and dynamic collaboration of people both internal and external to CAMH.

We began with a core team of CAMH addiction and mental health professionals—Dr. Bruce Ballon, Colleen Kelly, Sharon Labonte-Jaques and Joanne Shenfeld—who identified the central issues of concern to young children whose parents have a problem with alcohol. Gretchen Kelbaugh was hired to write a fictional story addressing these issues in a way that was understandable and accessible to kids. Addiction and mental health professionals specializing in substance use problems in the family reviewed the material and provided helpful feedback. Parents and children with first-hand knowledge of alcohol problems also reviewed the book and provided additional insight. Finally, Ben Hodson brought the whole thing to life with beautiful illustrations.

ACKNOWLEDGMENTS

Centre for Addiction and Mental Health Project and Writing Team

Susan Rosenstein, MA—Project Manager and Product Developer

Bruce Ballon, MD, FRCPC—Psychiatrist; Fellowships in Addiction and Child Psychiatry; Assistant Professor, University of Toronto, Clinician Education Specialist; Addiction Education Co-ordinator, CAMH

Colleen Kelly, MSW, RSW—Family Therapist, Family and Youth Addiction Programs, CAMH

Sharon Labonte-Jaques, Project Consultant, Education and Health Promotion, CAMH

Joanne Shenfeld, MSW., RSW—Service Manager, Family and Youth Addiction Services, CAMH

Writer for Hire—Gretchen Kelbaugh, Story First Productions

Illustrator—Ben Hodson

Special thanks to the following professionals who reviewed early versions of this book, provided invaluable insight and feedback on text and illustrations, and facilitated reviews by families:

Mary Austin, Administrative Secretary, CAMH

Kirstin Bindseil, Advanced Practice Clinician, Day/Residential Program, CAMH

Joanne Brown, Program Director, Parent Action on Drugs (PAD), Toronto, Ontario

Diane Buhler, Executive Director, Parent Action on Drugs (PAD), Toronto, Ontario

Gloria Chaim, Project Manager, Pathways to Healthy Families, The Jean Tweed Centre, Toronto, Ontario

Diana Dickey, Pathways to Healthy Families, The Jean Tweed Centre, Toronto, Ontario

Barb Farkus, Addiction Counsellor, Women's Day/Residential Program, CAMH

Jane Fjeld, Youth Priority Knowledge Exchange Manager, CAMH

Lew Golding, Manager of the Substance Abuse Program for African Canadian and Caribbean Youth (SAPACCY), CAMH

Larry Grand, Project Consultant, CAMH

Julia Greenbaum, Publishing Developer, CAMH

Dennis James, Deputy Clinical Director, Addictions Program, CAMH

Andrew Johnson, Publishing Developer, CAMH

Karen Leslie, MD, FRCPC, Staff Paediatrician, Substance Abuse Program, The Hospital for Sick Children; Associate Professor of Paediatrics, University of Toronto, Toronto, Ontario

Katherine Lo, Administrative Secretary, CAMH

Drupati Maharaj, Diversity Knowledge Exchange Manager, CAMH

Geetha Manohar, Administrative Secretary, CAMH

Lisle McGuigan, Early Childhood Development Consultant— Infant Toddler Specialist, Pathways To Healthy Families, The Jean Tweed Centre, Toronto

Lynn McGuigan, Independent Author, Guelph, Ontario

Ishwar Persad, Education and Training Specialist, Diversity Trainer, CAMH

Dr. David Wolfe, RBC Chair in Children's Mental Health, CAMH

Information for adults

Children have a lot of questions and fears when someone in their family drinks too much alcohol, especially a parent. Too much may be different for each person. Too much is when alcohol use has a negative impact on the person or on others. Alcohol problems easily become the family secret that no one talks about. It's a secret that affects the whole family.

The goal of this book is two-fold. We want to give young children (five to 10 years old) a storybook that holds their interest and provides helpful and easy-to-understand answers to their most common questions. At the same time, we want to offer a tool to help you (the parent, grandparent, teacher, addiction or mental health professional or other concerned adult) talk with children about an alcohol problem in the family. We've made sure to incorporate diversity both in the storyline and the illustrations, so the book is highly accessible and relevant to a broad range of children. Encouraging children to start talking to you and others about family issues related to an alcohol problem is one of the most important things you can do for them.

Remember, alcohol problems in the family are complex. This book is not intended to replace professional help. Please get help from a professional.

Why talk about the parent who drinks too much?
Children tend to have common questions when a parent has a problem with alcohol. Research has shown that good communication within a family is related to a child's ability to make healthy, positive choices in difficult life situations. Good communication contributes to their resilience or ability to cope with adversity.

Children often understand more than you might think. They need to be able to ask questions, even though it's often hard for them to do so. And they need answers to their questions, even though the questions themselves are difficult. The answers must be clear, concise and appropriate for the child's age and ability to understand.

There is also evidence that having a caring, trustworthy, healthy adult in children's lives can help protect children from the negative effects of a parent's drinking. This person may be the other parent, a grandparent, teacher, aunt/uncle or parent of a friend. It is all right for children to reach out for help and it's fine for them to talk about their problems.

It's common for kids to worry about whether or not their parent will ever be able to stop drinking, and whether they have somehow caused their parent's drinking. When children don't get accurate information, they often come to their own conclusions. Their ideas may be wrong and frightening. Children need to hear over and over again that the parent's drinking problem is not their fault.

There are a number of ways you can encourage children to talk about what it's like having a parent with an alcohol problem. If your children are open to talking, this story can be the focal point of your conversation. It can give you ways to explain the alcohol problem. If your children are not open to talking, simply reading the story will let them know that the questions they think about are the same ones that other children have. Talking about these thoughts will likely help them to feel less alone and confused. Over time, they may feel better able to talk about their feelings, fears, wishes and worries.

Note: *If a health care provider or a person who performs professional or official duties with children suspects that a parent or guardian's substance use may be physically or emotionally harming his or her child, this person has a legal responsibility to report this to children's protection agencies, such as the Children's Aid Society (CAS). If you are concerned about a person's legal or ethical responsibility, discuss this issue with him or her.*

Information for kids

Hi kids,

Wishes and Worries describes your life, doesn't it?

We know that it's really hard to be a kid, especially when your mom or dad drinks too much. We also know that you may worry about all kinds of things. You may be worried that:

- your mom or dad drinks because of you

- the drinking problem is going to get worse

- your family is really different

- friends won't want to play at your house

- things never feel calm or safe at home.

We also know that you probably wish that things would get better and that your mom or dad would stop drinking. You may also wish that your family wasn't so different from your friends' families.

We hope this story helps you better understand what is going on in your family. The main character in the story, Maggie, probably has some of the same kinds of experiences that you have. Her dad drinks too much. She learns that there are some adults in her life that she can trust and talk to. She also learns that there are some things she can do to help herself, like staying involved in sports and activities, drawing in her art book, and calling a kids' help line. Maggie hopes that her father will be able to stop drinking and that things will be better for her whole family.

We hope you will try to help yourself in some of the ways Maggie does. And most of all, we want you to understand that *you didn't cause your mom or dad's drinking problem and that it's not your job to fix it.*

People you can talk to:

- Kids Help Phone (in Canada):
  1 800 668-6868,
  24 hours a day, seven days a week

- a teacher

- a counsellor or therapist

- a family doctor

- family members
  (aunts, uncles, grandparents)

- your close friend's parents

Your people to talk to:

Name: _____

Address: _____

_____

Phone number: _____

Name: _____

Address: _____

_____

Phone number: _____

Nine candles on my chocolate cake. It's time to make a wish and I know what it is. I wish that the rest of my birthday party won't fall apart like last year. What a mess that was.

Last year's party started out great. Mom let me have eight friends from school. Eight years old. Eight friends. And guess who came? Amanda Li, one of my favourite new friends! We play at school, but I've been too embarrassed to have her come to my house. My family is kind of different.

Dad's one job was to bring the cake home before the party. It was his only job because he always lets us down when we count on him to do things. He's either late or he doesn't even show up.

As usual, he was late and got home just as the party was starting. He had on his silly smile, but he had the cake—an ice cream cake. Then it happened. He was walking funny and tripped as he went to put the cake on the table. He dropped the whole thing right on top of Candy, our dog, who started licking it off the floor and off her fur. Then Mom and Dad started yelling at each other in front of my friends. Everyone was so shocked they didn't know what to do. We were all embarrassed. The party was a total disaster.

That night, my family sat down to watch me open my presents. There was my older sister, Beth, my little brother, Daniel, and me, Maggie. Our family likes to be together like this for birthdays. It's usually fun. That night, as if Dad hadn't ruined everything else, he tripped as he walked into the room, and then fell asleep on the couch. He started snoring just as I was opening the first present. I was really annoyed. Beth got so mad that she left to go hang out with her friends.

"Dad bought you a new bicycle," Mom said, hoping that this would make me feel better. "It's bright green. Let's go out and see it."

"No thanks," I said. I'd rather Dad gave me a little present and cared enough to watch me open it. "Why can't you wake Dad up?" I asked. "I miss it when he doesn't do things with the rest of the family."

"You know he'll just be grumpy and angry, Maggie," Mom said. That really made me sad.

I told you my family was different.

The next day in school, my friends ignored me. I heard Amanda whispering that my dad was drunk at my party. I was so hurt and angry that I knocked her lunch bag on the floor. Then I felt bad and started crying, and that's when my teacher, Mr. Hubble, came over.

I thought I'd get in trouble, but I didn't. First he told the other kids to go outside for recess. Then he said Amanda Li shouldn't talk behind my back, and I shouldn't knock anyone's lunch on the floor. "Maggie," he said. "Why are you so angry?"

He wanted to know why *I* was angry! And he was being really nice. I wanted so badly to talk to someone, but could I trust him? Would he be a safe person to talk to? Then I remembered when my friend Max told Mr. Hubble about his parents' divorce. Max said Mr. Hubble was a great listener.

I took a deep breath and started talking. "I got so upset and embarrassed at my birthday party. My friends saw everything. Now they are telling people that my dad was drunk. My parents had a big fight. It's such a mess," I said.

I talked and talked. It felt so good to tell someone about the problems going on at home. Mr. Hubble said, "Maybe your dad drinks too much alcohol, Maggie. Some people who drink too much can't stop, and end up saying and doing things that really hurt people they love."

"But why does Dad do it?" I asked.

"Some people drink because they are sad or have bad things going on in their lives. I think you should talk to Miss Ye, our school counsellor. Lots of kids like to talk to her. There are tons of families like yours."

That was good to know! It's helpful to talk to someone you trust about what you're thinking and feeling. Your feelings are OK.

When I went home I was too scared to tell Mom. I thought she'd be really mad that I told our family secrets to my teacher. Mom had too much to worry about already.

But you know what? She came into my bedroom and talked to me about Dad's drinking and the party. "Dad and I both love you and are trying to make things better, Maggie. Dad's drinking isn't your fault." I felt better than I'd felt in a long time.

Mom and Dad just saw our family doctor, Dr. Gupta. The doctor explained that Dad drinks too much alcohol but that there are people like her to help take care of him. She said that we shouldn't blame ourselves for Dad's bad decisions. No matter what my brother, sister and I do, Dad's drinking problem is not our fault.

All this time I thought that my parents argued because of us. Daniel tries so hard to be good. He is usually really quiet so Dad doesn't have anything to yell at him about. Beth tries to be perfect. We always feel like we're walking on eggshells. We're scared because we don't know what Dad will do next.

But now Mom and Dad have some good news. Dad has his own counsellor and he and Mom are going to work on this problem together. Wow. Maybe some day things at home will get better. For now, Dad's stopped drinking.

The next day at school, I went to see Miss Ye. Her smile goes right across her face. We talked a lot about when someone you love drinks too much alcohol, and how it can affect the whole family.

"You didn't cause this problem, Maggie," she said. "And it's not your problem to fix. Sometimes you and your brother and sister may feel upset by what's going on at home. It's important to talk to an adult you trust."

"Like my Gramps!" I said. "I can call him whenever I feel like it. I can also walk next door to our neighbour Melda's house if things are bad at home." Miss Ye told me that those were great ideas.

On the way home from school, I started to worry that Mom might start having problems with alcohol too. So I asked her when I got home.

"Mom, do you think you will start drinking too much like Dad?"

"That's never been a problem for me, Maggie," she said. "But I don't drink with Dad, in case he feels tempted to drink too."

"So people can drink and not have problems?" I asked.

"A lot of people do that," she said.

"Why does anyone drink, if it can cause so many problems?"

This was hard for Mom to answer. She said that alcohol is only a problem for some people. At first, drinking can make people feel happy or more relaxed. But if you drink too much you get drunk, and that can make you feel tired, angry, sad or even sick to your tummy. It can even make you feel sick the next day.

Once Dad was upset late at night. I thought it was because of my report card. He was crying and things were thrown around the room. It was a mess!! Now I see that he was sad and angry because he had been drinking.

I wish I had known then that I didn't make him upset—that it wasn't my fault.

About six months later, Dad and I had a talk.

"Maggie, I'm really starting to feel better about myself," he said. "Until your eighth birthday party (the one where the cake ended up on Candy's head), I didn't even know my drinking was a problem. Now I know that it affects the whole family. I'm trying hard not to drink anymore."

"I know you are, Dad," I said.

Then Dad held my hand. He hadn't done this in a long time. "I'm sorry for all the trouble I've caused," he said. "I want you to know that I love you kids so much."

"I love you too, Dad," I said.

We were both crying a little. We'd been feeling a lot closer ever since we'd been spending more time together. "It was fun at your basketball game yesterday," he said. "I was so proud of you."

A few weeks later, Grandma, Dad's mother, came for a visit. She said she was so glad that Dad was getting the help he needed. She knows that too much alcohol can hurt the whole family. She said that Grandpa once had a problem with alcohol. When I heard that, I began to worry it would happen to me.

"Grandma, do you think I might start drinking too much too?"

"Maggie, I don't think that will happen to you," Grandma said.
"You have so many things in your life that make you happy.
And you seem to be really good at talking about your feelings!"

Miss Ye told me to take up hobbies I enjoy. So I listen to music, draw in my art book, play on the basketball team and sing in the school choir. Daniel doesn't even plug his ears now when he hears me sing. He and Dad come to my basketball games and my whole family came to hear me at music night last month.

I'm doing way better in school now. One reason I can study better is that I don't have to worry about how to help Dad. It's not my problem to figure out. I'll stick to figuring out math.

One day Beth was babysitting Daniel and me. She surprised us by getting us our favourite treat—a huge bag of potato chips.

She started talking about our family. "Once, when Dad's drinking was really bad, I called a kids help line."

"What's that?" I asked.

"It's a special, safe telephone number for kids only. It's really great. When I called, I talked and talked about how scared and worried I was. The counsellor just listened. She said lots of kids call and say they feel the same way."

Beth said she found the number in the phone book. She gave us the number so Daniel and I can try it too.

Things seemed to be going so well. It was spring and we were excited to ride our bikes again. But then . . . Dad ran over my bike with the car, even though I'd left it on the grass. I remembered that Miss Ye said that when people are trying to stop drinking, they might still slip and start drinking again. Looks like that's what happened.

Mom said people make bad decisions when they drink, so Dad shouldn't have been driving a car. Duh! Everyone knows you shouldn't drink and drive.

Dr. Gupta told him to try to stop drinking again. She told him to work fewer hours, spend more time with the family and do the hobbies he used to enjoy. Dad started gardening and planted a bunch of herbs and vegetables. By the end of the summer, I was so sick of eating green things.

Now it's September 15, my ninth birthday. Dad hasn't been drunk since that time he broke my bike. But here I am again with my friends, sitting around the table waiting for Dad, who is late. . . . I'm so scared that he may be drinking again. My one wish is that he won't come home drunk and mess up my party like last year.

I blow out the candles and everyone claps. Just then the door opens. It's Dad and he's covered in green paint. I'm about to tell all the girls (nine this year) to start eating the cake when Dad hands me a bright, neon green bike helmet with cool racing stripes.

"Go see what's outside, Maggie," he said.

Leaning against the fence is my bicycle, fixed and repainted shiny green. Wow, it looks better than ever.

Then Dad gave me a hug. "I hope you have a really happy birthday this year." Boy, was it ever.

"Let's go for a ride!" said Amanda Li to all of us girls. We race each other to get on our bikes. Tamara gets going the fastest, but I don't mind. I don't even care that I haven't had a chance to eat my birthday cake yet! I'm just so happy that Dad hasn't been drinking. I know it will be really hard for him to stop drinking forever. There will probably be more ups and downs. But I really hope he can do it. That's my biggest wish of all.